I ♥ WINE!

An Odd Squad book about ladies for LADIES!
by Allan Plenderleith

ℛℛ
RAVETTE PUBLISHING

First Published by
Ravette Publishing Limited 2005
Unit 3, Tristar Centre, Star Road, Partridge Green,
West Sussex RH13 8RA

Printed and bound in Malta

ISBN: 1 84161 239 1

Maude decides to cut down to just
one glass of wine a night.

As the light came on, the burglar realised he wasn't the only one in the room with a bushy beard

Maude gets a boob job.

As Maude approached middle age,
her bum had sadly moved south.

In her later years, Lily had to resort to desperate measures to banish wrinkles.

To prevent forehead wrinkles, Maude got
some buttocks injections.

Suddenly, the hairdresser realised he'd left
Lily a bit too long under the dryer.

It was so cold that Lily's nipples were visible.

Maude was always getting her
cleavage out in public.

Jeff knew when Maude was drunk
she would eat ANYTHING!

Why you should never wear fruity lip gloss
on a sunny day.

Things EVERY WOMAN should have in her HANDBAG!

1. EMERGENCY CHOCOLATE RATION!
   For when the evil cravings come!

2. JAR OF FART GAS!
   For clearing busy shops of annoying queues!

. YOUR MAN'S CREDIT CARD!
For those 'emergency' purchases!

4. A SMALL POO!
For scaring away annoying children!

. A BABY MAGAZINE!
For scaring away annoying men!

To find out if a man is going to be good
in bed, simply buy him a cream doughnut.

To her surprise, Maude arrived home to find
Jeff doing the dishes.

After limping for several blocks,
Maude was relieved to find her high heels
weren't broken after all.

At her party, Maude serves up her
guests some homemade punch.

During the disco, Maude finds an embarrassing ladder in her tights.

Having slept in again, Maude was late for work and had to apply her make-up on the train.

HOW TO BE A COMPLETE BITCH!

1. FIT AN ELECTRIC CURRENT TO THE TOILET SEAT TO STOP MEN PEEING ON THE SEAT!

4. PRETEND TO FALL ASLEEP DURING SEX!

During boring sex, Lily likes to pass the time by playing with Alf's excessively hairy bum.

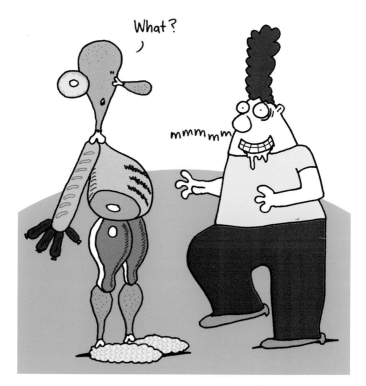

It was the 2nd day of Maude's diet,
and Jeff was somehow looking very attractive.

Maude only realised she'd taken a long time to get ready for her night out when she stepped outside.

For her birthday, Maude got
some nail extensions.

Tired of waiting in queues for night club loos,
Maude thinks of a better plan.

Unfortunately, it took Maude a few seconds to realise she had not, in fact, answered her vibrating mobile.

Sadly, Maude couldn't have sex that night
because she 'had the painters in.'

2. HAVE A LARGE SUPPLY OF CHOCOLATE AND WINE NEARBY AT ALL TIMES!

5. USE THE BEST PAIN KILLER ON THE MARKET – BOOZE!

Why older women should avoid
going on roundabouts.

FUN USES for SAGGY BAPS!

A CHILD'S SKIPPING ROPE!

TYING UP CRIMINALS

RETRACTABLE DOG LEAD!

BOING!

BALLOON ANIMALS AT KIDS' PARTIES!

AAAAAAAAA!!

Unfortunately, Maude's skirt was so short that when she bent down everyone saw her kebab.

Like most women, Maude was obsessed about the size of her butt.

To turn Jeff on, Maude dresses up in
her old school uniform.

Always take your tampon out BEFORE
going in the bath.

Reasons why SHOPPING is GOOD FOR YOU!

1. GREAT EXERCISE
AS YOU COMPARE PRICES IN EVERY CLOTHES SHOP IN TOWN

2. IMPROVES OBSERVATION
AS YOU HUNT FOR THOSE ELUSIVE SALE SIGNS

3. STRENGTHENS ARMS
WHEN CARRYING HUNDREDS OF BAGS LOADED WITH DISCOUNT GOODS

4. IMPROVES SELF-DEFENSE SKILLS AS YOU BATTLE THE SALES VULTURES FOR THE BEST BARGAINS

POW!

PAM!

REDUCED BIN

5. IMPROVES MATHEMATICAL SKILLS

AS YOU TRY TO CALCULATE HOW MUCH YOU HAVE LEFT ON YOUR CREDIT CARD!

Even when she was drunk,
Maude could take her face off.

Suddenly, during her sexy dance,
Maude's suspenders snap.

Maude's constant texting had taken its toll.

Although fun at the time, Maude later regretted having sex on the stairs.

Unfortunately, Jeff's tan line gave away what they had been doing on the beach all day yesterday.

QUALITY

FOR A GOOD QUALITY WINE, GO FOR PRETTY LABELS, LOTS OF FOREIGN WORDS AND A PRICE OVER £1.99

OPENING

AFTER YOU BREAK THE CORK IN HALF AS USUAL AND FAIL TO GET THE REST OUT, SIMPLY SMASH THE NECK OFF!

DRINKING

TAKE A TINY SIP, TRY TO
SAY SOMETHING VAGUELY
INTELLIGENT, THEN GLUG
THE REST DOWN AS FAST
AS POSSIBLE!

FOOD

TO COMPLIMENT THE
DELICATE LAYERED
FLAVOURS OF THE WINE,
CHOOSE SOMETHING
CHEESY.

Who needs tassels to perform sexy swinging boob dances when you have excess nipple hair!

To make herself look more buxom,
Maude stuffed tissues down her bra.

THE ODD SQUAD GUIDE TO
TRAINING A MAN!

1. CONDITION HIS THINKING TO BELIEVE THE MORE HOUSEWORK HE DOES = MORE SEX!

WAAHEY-OW!

2. PINCH HIM WHEN HIS TEAM SCORES. HE'LL SOON ASSOCIATE PAIN WITH SPORT AND STOP WATCHING!

3. ATTACH A SMALL ELECTRIC CURRENT TO THE TOILET SEAT TO PREVENT HIM SPLASHING ALL OVER IT!

4. CARRY A LARGE BAT AROUND WITH YOU FOR WHEN HE LETS ONE GO!

Maude had that other version of V.P.L.
...Visible Poo Line.

The 'Who can do the Biggest Fart Game' goes awry when Maude loses control for a second.

HOW TO FIGHT THE SIGNS OF AGEING!

1. APPLY WRINKLE CREAM LIBERALLY – PREFERABLY WITH A TROWEL!

2. PREVENT "OLD LADY TASH" BY SHAVING EVERY HOUR

. SPRAY REGULARLY WITH EXTRA STRENGTH PERFUME TO MASK THE SMELL OF DECAY

4. RAISE YOUR SAGGY BOOBS BY TYING A COUPLE OF KNOTS IN THEM!

Other ODD SQUAD books available ...

		ISBN	Price
The Odd Squad's Big Poo Handbook	(hardcover)	1 84161 168 9	£7.99
The Odd Squad's Sexy Sex Manual	(hardcover)	1 84161 220 0	£7.99
The Odd Squad Butt Naked		1 84161 190 5	£3.99
The Odd Squad Gross Out!		1 84161 219 7	£3.99
The Odd Squad's Saggy Bits		1 84161 218 9	£3.99
The REAL Kama Sutra		1 84161 103 4	£3.99
The Odd Squad Volume One		1 85304 936 0	£3.99
I Love Beer!	(hardcover)	1 84161 238 3	£4.99
I Love Sex!	(hardcover)	1 84161 241 3	£4.99
I Love Poo!	(hardcover)	1 84161 240 5	£4.99
The Odd Squad's Little Book of Booze		1 84161 138 7	£2.50
The Odd Squad's Little Book of Men		1 84161 093 3	£2.50
The Odd Squad's Little Book of Oldies		1 84161 139 5	£2.50
The Odd Squad's Little Book of Poo		1 84161 096 8	£2.50
The Odd Squad's Little Book of Pumping		1 84161 140 9	£2.50
The Odd Squad's Little Book of Sex		1 84161 095 X	£2.50
The Odd Squad's Little Book of Women		1 84161 094 1	£2.50
The Odd Squad's Little Book of X-Rated Cartoons		1 84161 141 7	£2.50

HOW TO ORDER: Please send a cheque/postal order in £ sterling, made payable to 'Ravette Publishing' for the cover price of the books and allow the following for post & packing ...

UK & BFPO	60p for the first book & 30p per book thereafter
Europe & Eire	£1.00 for the first book & 50p per book thereafter
Rest of the world	£1.80 for the first book & 80p per book thereafter

RAVETTE PUBLISHING
Unit 3, Tristar Centre, Star Road, Partridge Green, West Sussex RH13 8RA

Prices and availability are subject to change without prior notice.